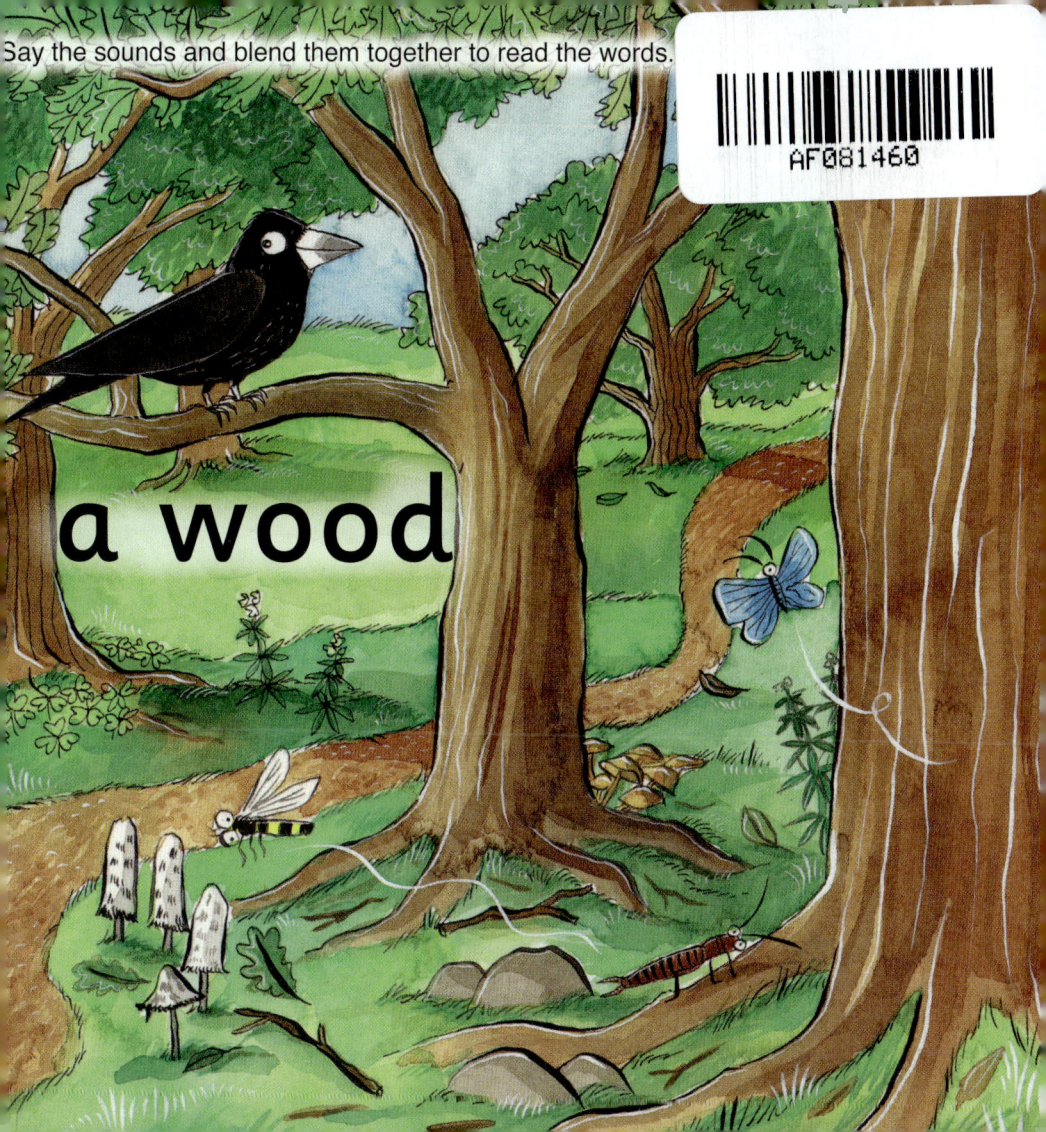

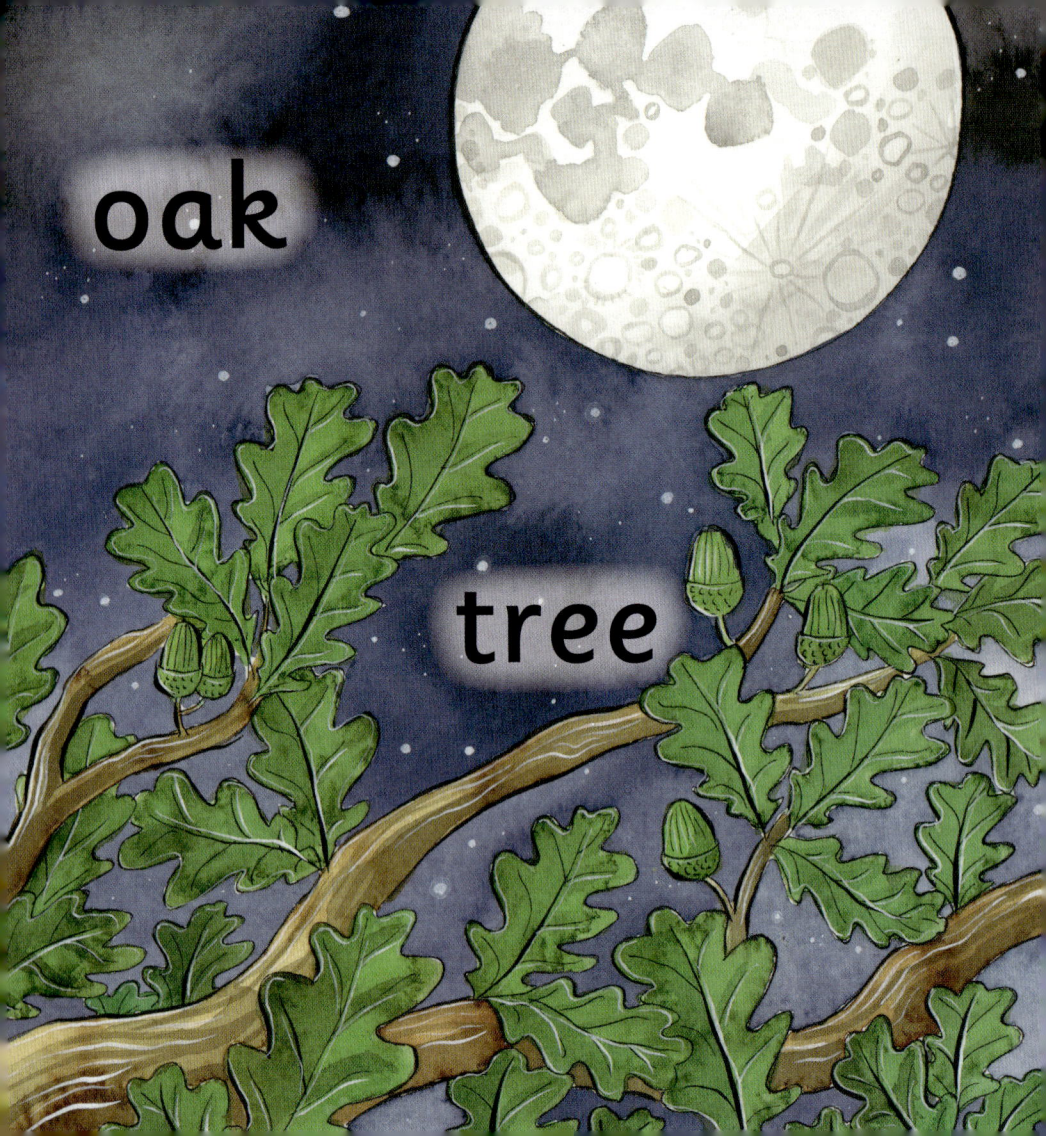

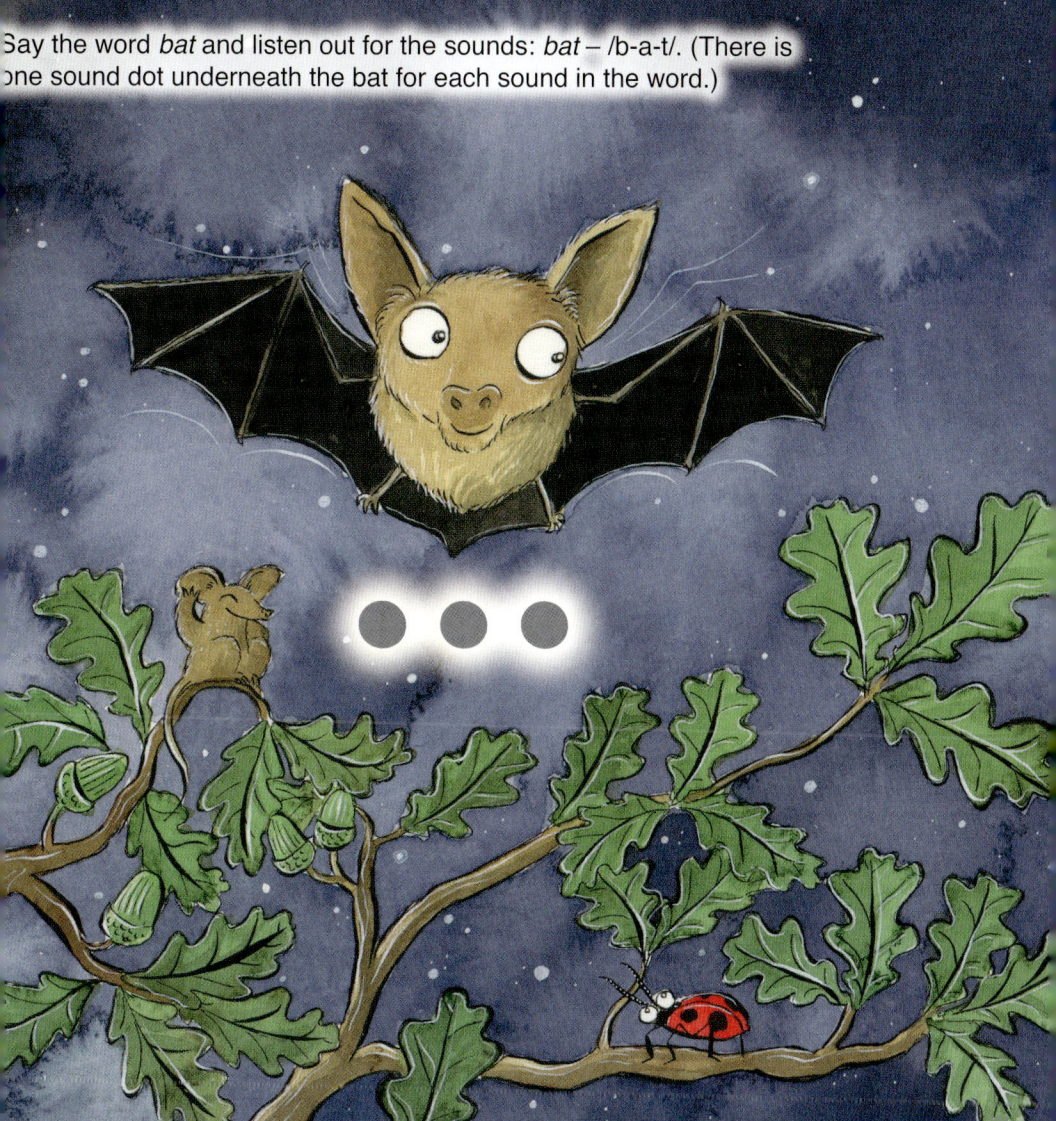
Say the word *bat* and listen out for the sounds: *bat* – /b-a-t/. (There is one sound dot underneath the bat for each sound in the word.)

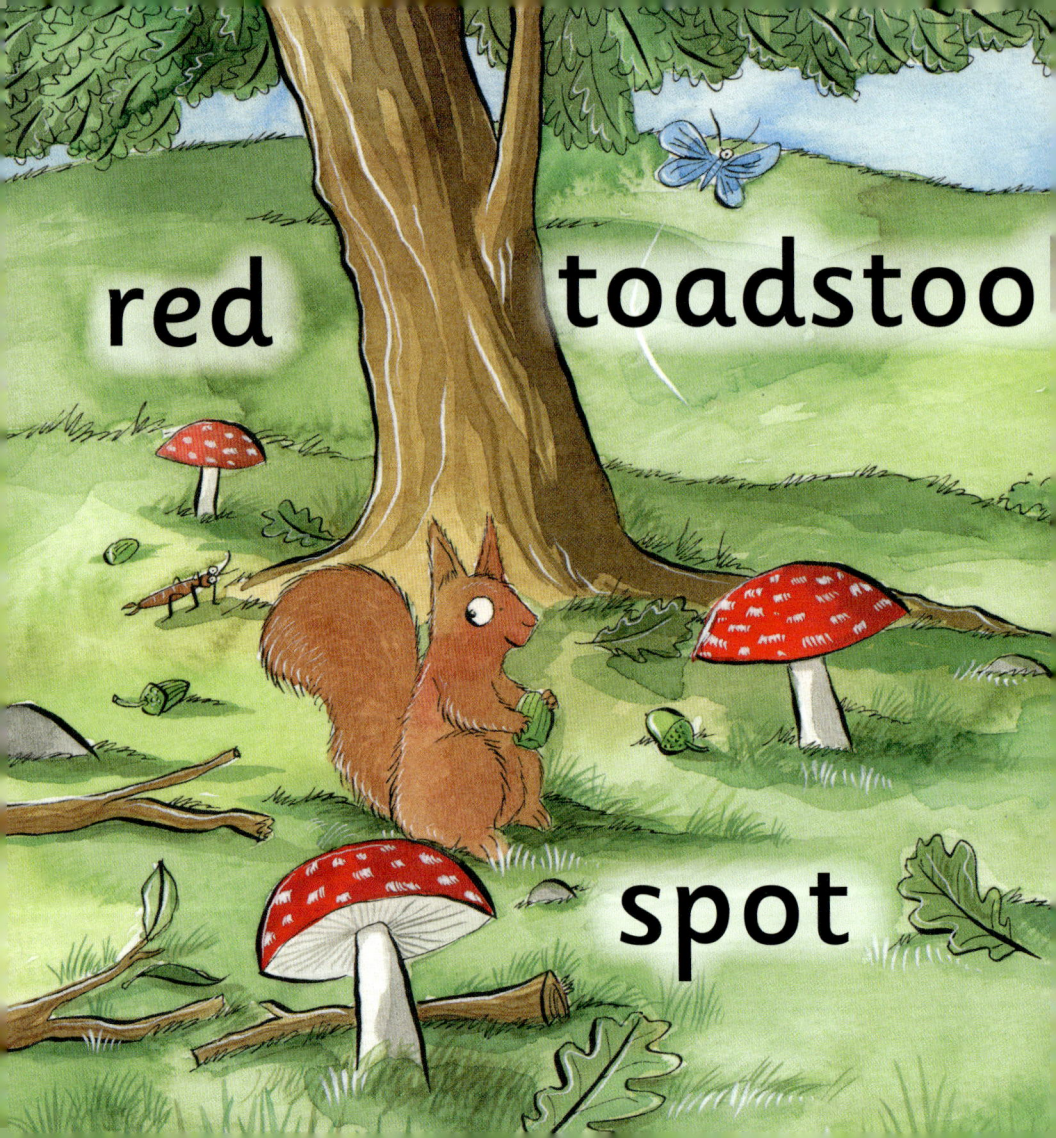

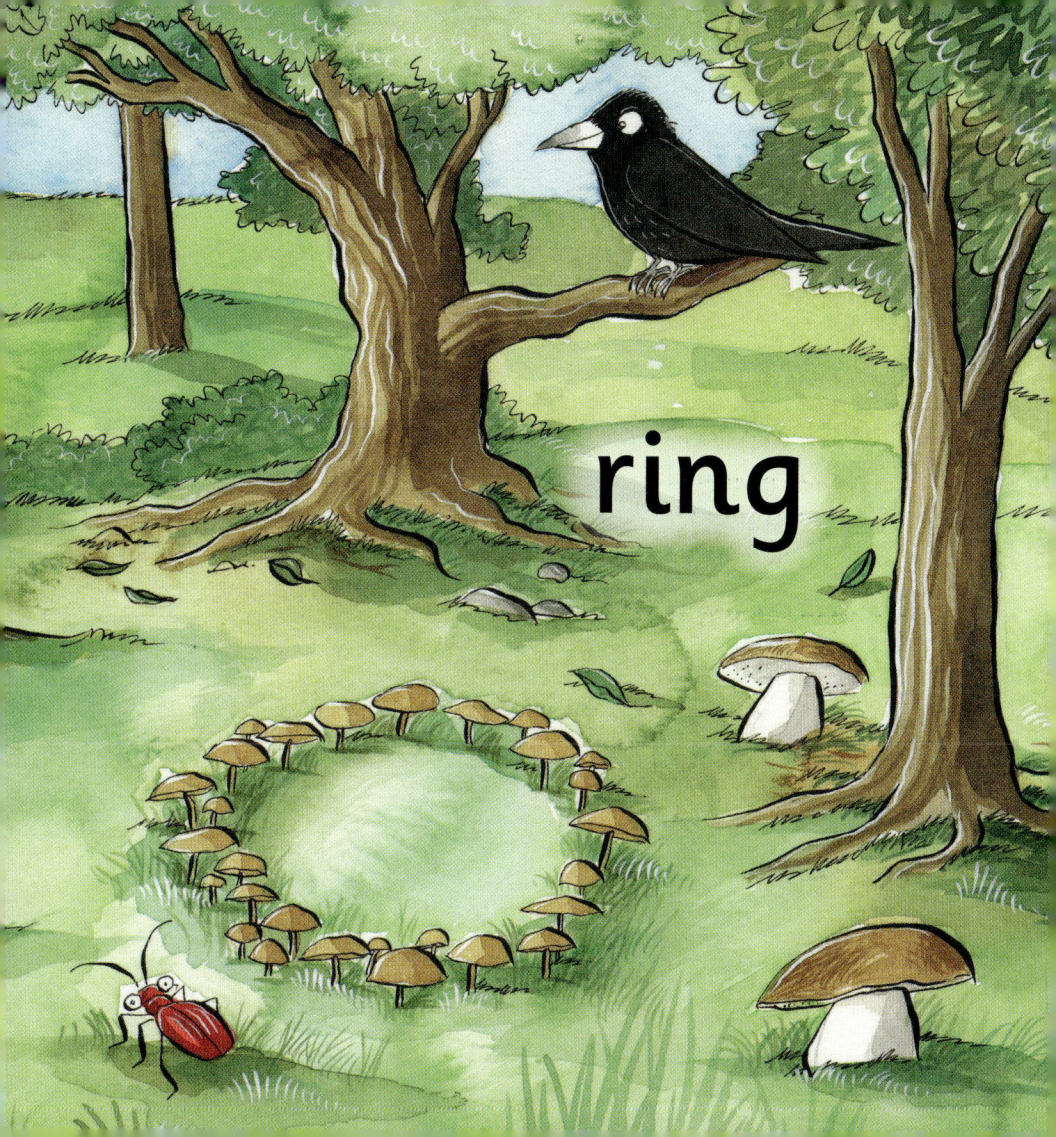

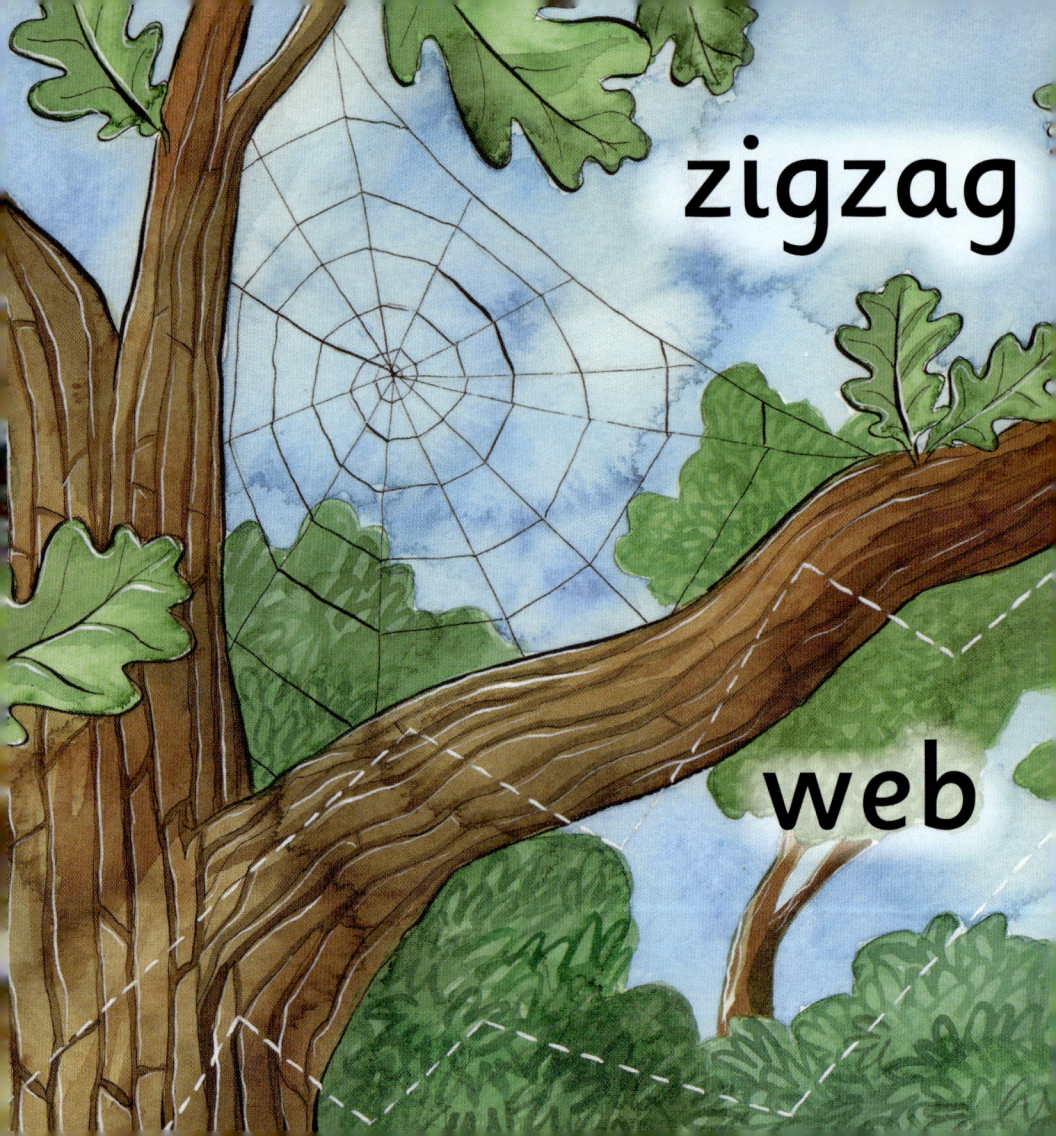

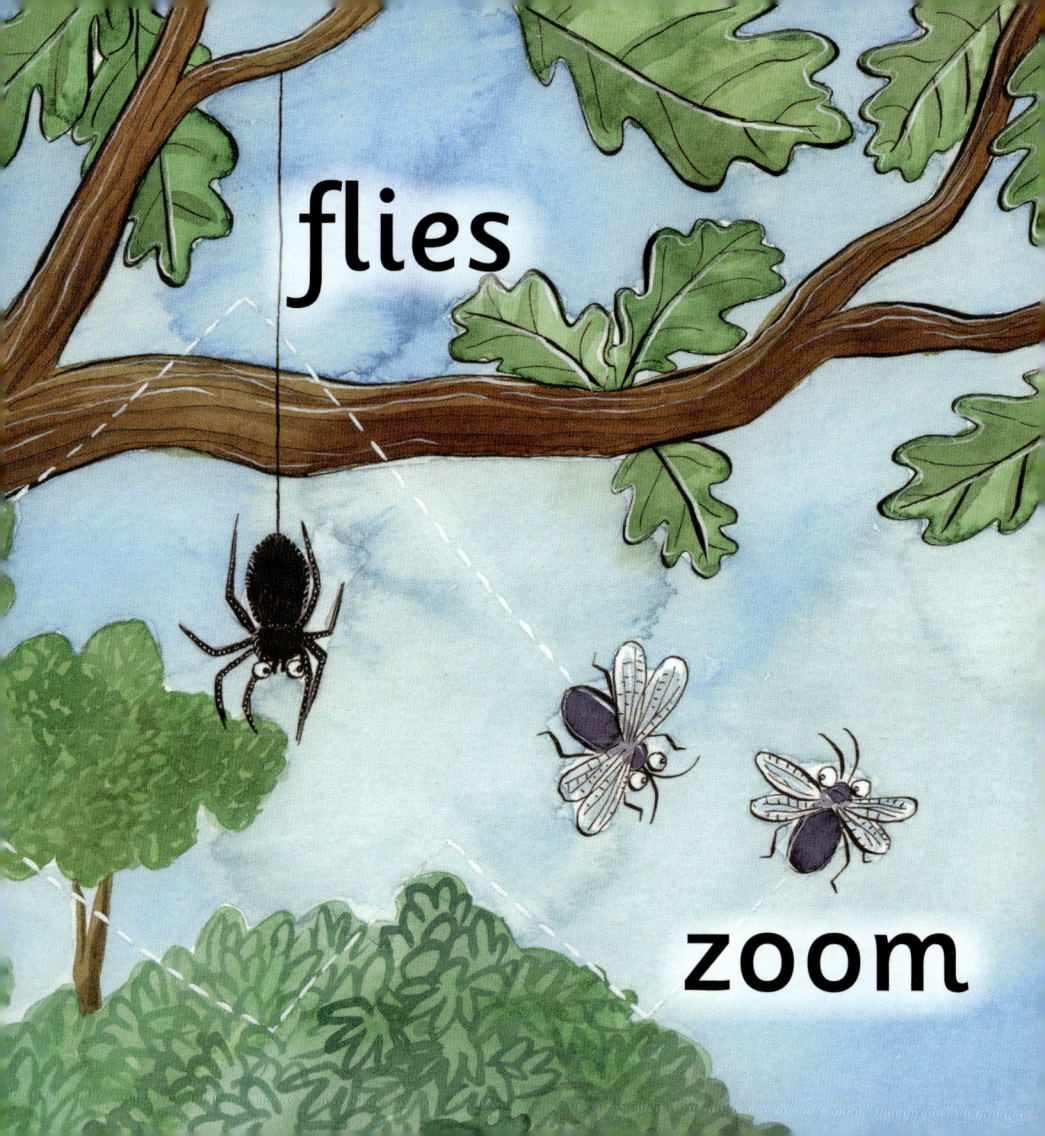

Look at the letters and say the sounds. See how quickly you can say all of them.

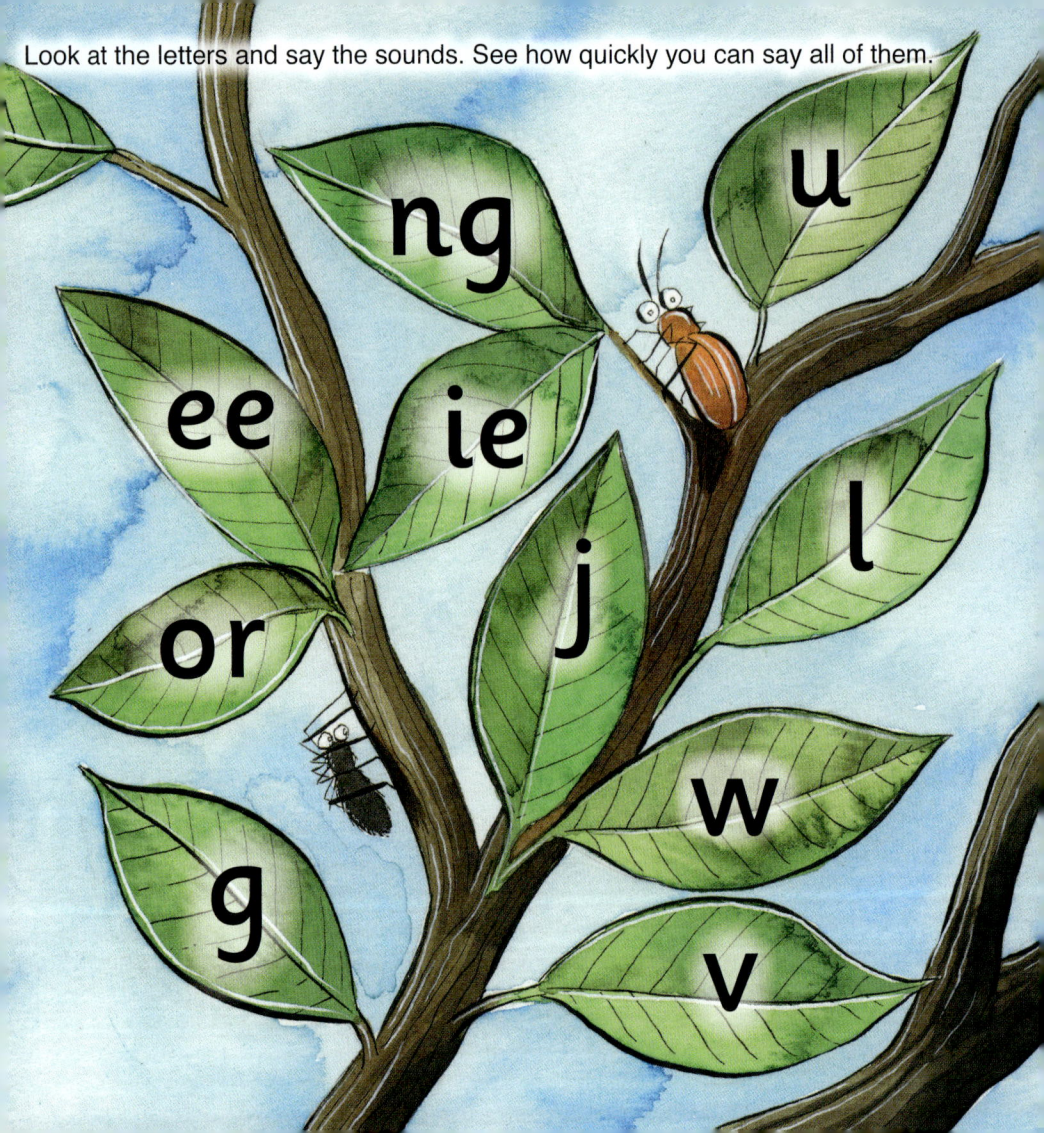

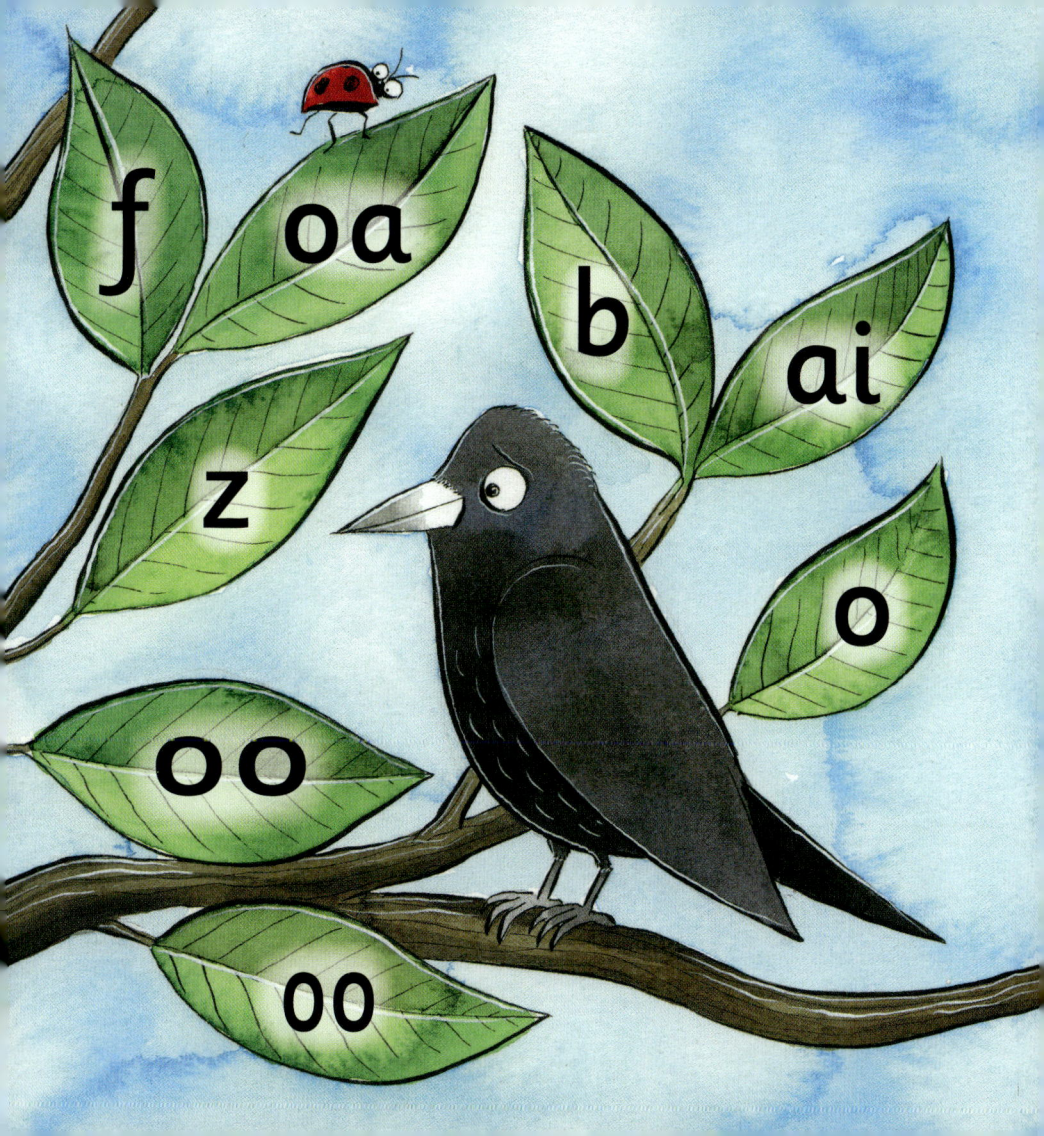

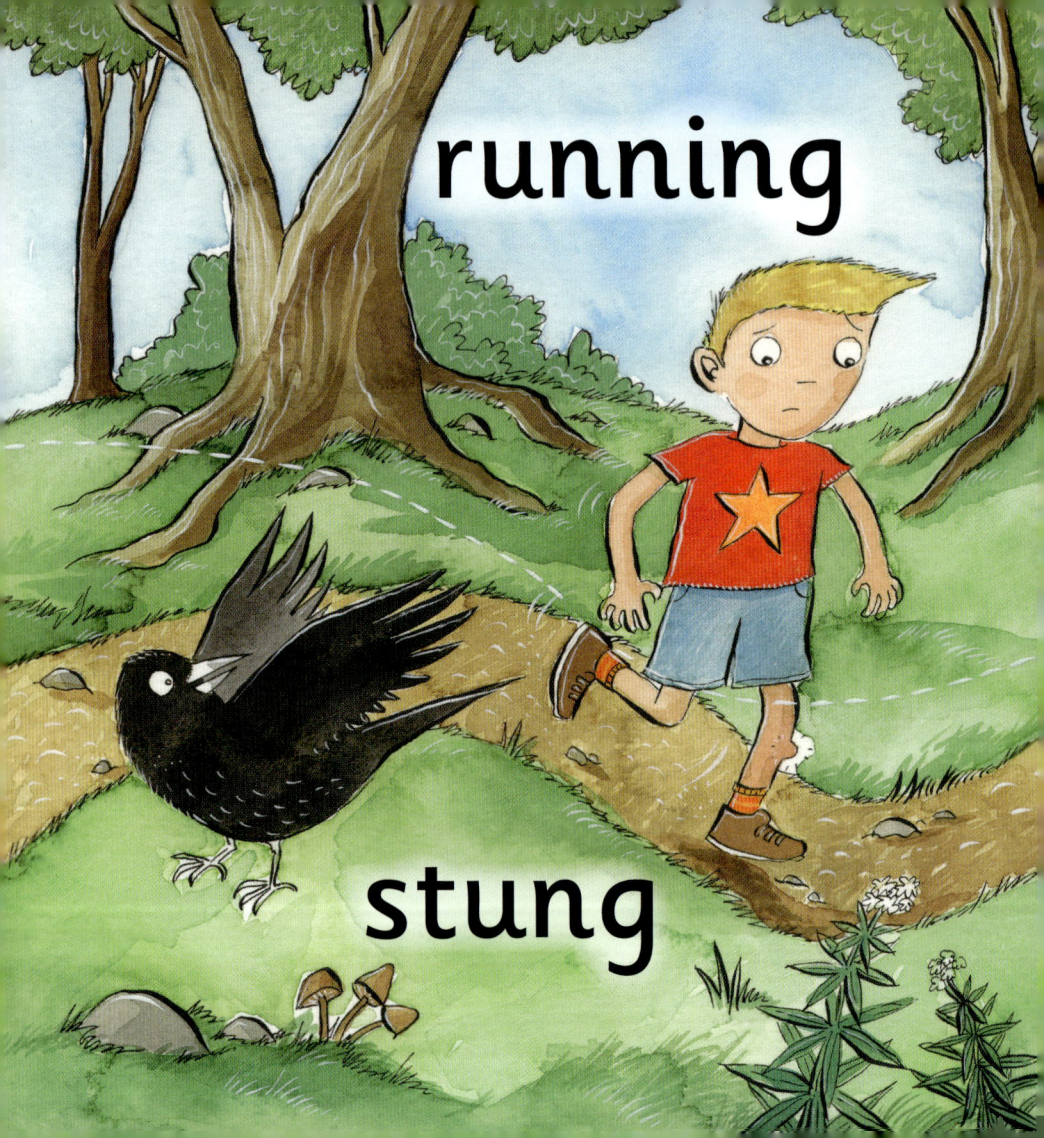

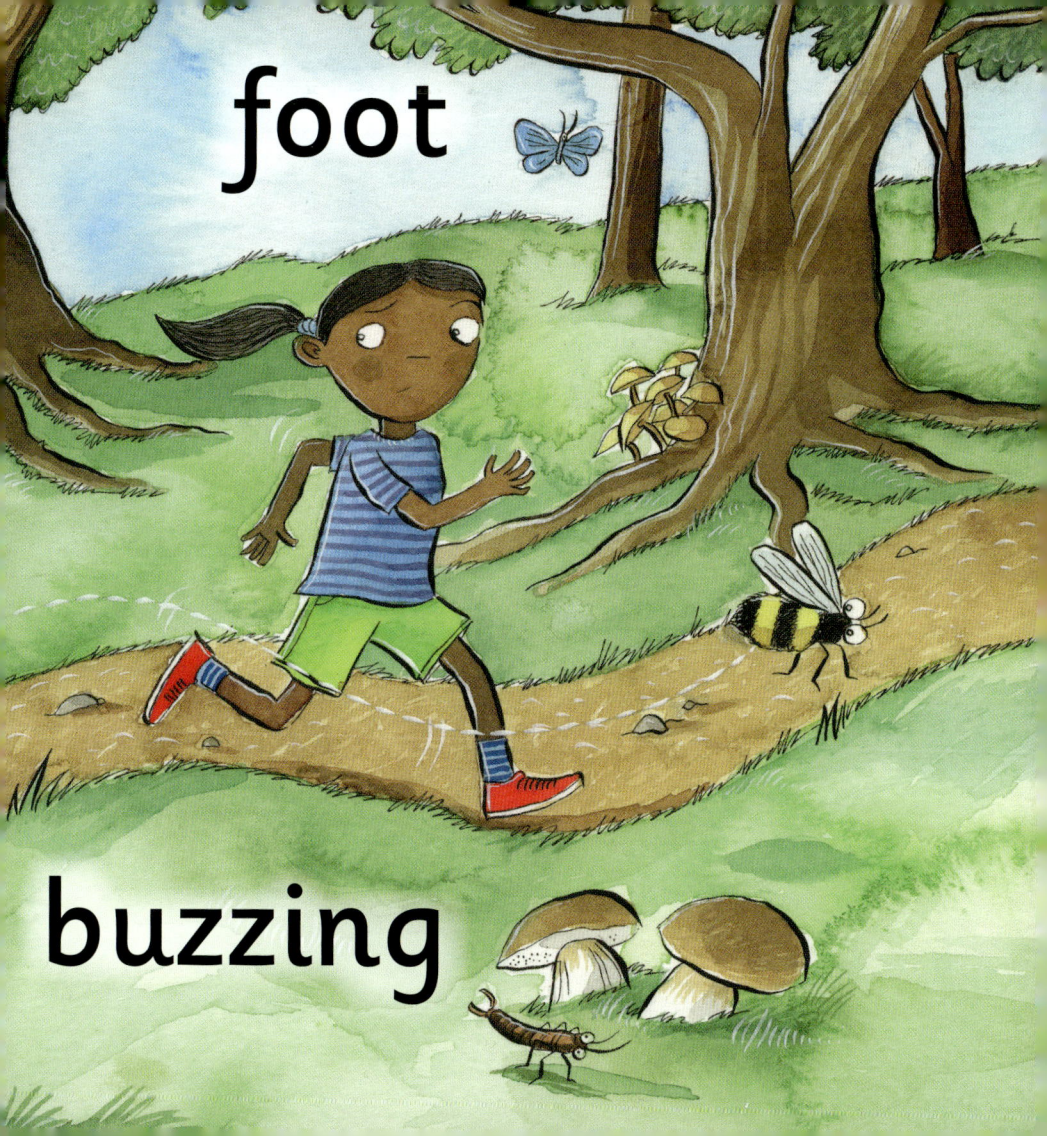

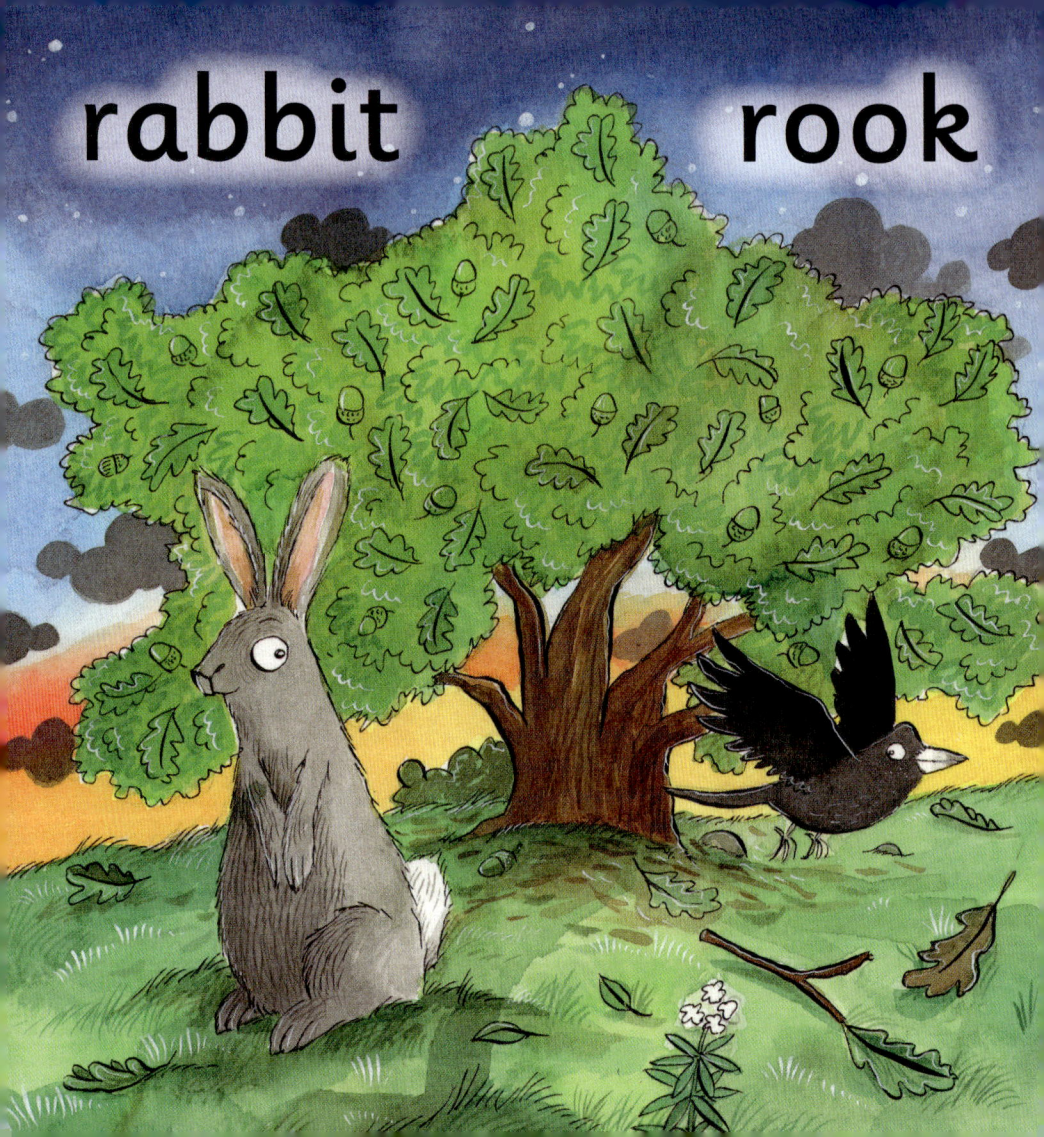